Prolance

www.prolancewriting.com
California, USA
© 2019 Heba Subeh-Hyder

ISBN: 978-1-7338267-3-0

Maymunah's Musings

HOW MUCH does ALLAH Love Me?

Written by:
Heba Subeh-Hyder

Illustrated by:
Aatena Hasan

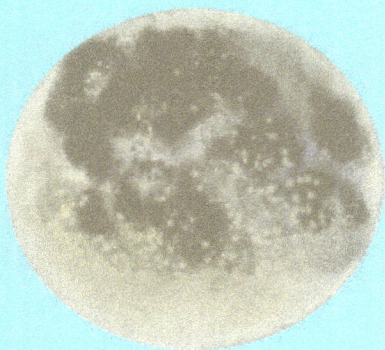

May Allah
accept my
efforts and
intention.

Bismillah
Ar-Rahman
Ar-Raheem

I owe everything I am and everything I have done to Allah, swt, for He is my Provider, my Protector, and through Him, I found, and will always find, my inspiration. Without Him, none of my dreams and aspirations would have come to fruition. I am forever grateful.

To my husband. My best friend, my rock, my companion, my champion, my partner, my support, and my soulmate. Without you, there is no me. And let's face it, there probably would be no book. As the wise Jerry Maguire once said, "You complete me."

To my three strong, intelligent daughters, who are beautiful inside and out. As cliche as this sounds, spread your wings and fly, my loves. Don't be afraid of where the wind takes you. As long as you seek Allah's pleasure, you will go to tremendous heights, inshallah.

To the rest of my loved ones. Thank you for your undying support and motivation, without which I would not have had the courage to start this special journey. I'm truly blessed to have you all in my life.

To everyone who purchased my book without knowing what they got themselves into, I thank you. And I hope it is to your liking.

Maymunah was a curious little girl, who often thought about Allah, subhanahu wa ta'ala. She was thinking about Him now as she gazed out into the hazy, indigo-colored evening sky, listening to the pitter-patter of raindrops against her windowpane.

She thought about all the magnificent things she learned about Allah in her Sunday school.

She thought about all the animals He created: big, small, fast, and slow.

She thought about the vast number of stars in the sky that looked like sparkling diamonds.

She thought about all the different types of trees: fruit trees, flowering trees, and trees that provide shade in the hot, summer days.

She thought about her family: her Mama, her Baba, and her brother and sister, and how much love she had in her heart for them.

But the one thing that Maymunah thought about the most was the love she had for Allah in the deepest part of her heart. She wondered, *how much does Allah love me?*

And with that thought, Maymunah rushed to the only person she knew would be able to give her an answer.

"Mama! Mama!" Maymunah cried out, running to her mother's study.

"Yes, habeebty? Are you alright?" Maymunah's mother was just finishing her daily Quran reading.

"Mama, I have a very important question for you that needs to be answered right away!" Maymunah said urgently.

"Well, then I hope to have an answer for this very important question, inshallah," her mother said with a smile.

"You know I love Allah very much. But what I don't know is...exactly how much does Allah love ME?" Maymunah was so eager to hear the answer, she hopped onto her mother's lap before her mother could even utter a word!

Her mother laughed as she scooped up little Maymunah in her arms, and said, "Well, now that is a very good, and VERY important question that needs answering right away, Maymunah."

"Allah loves you so very much, my dear. He loves you more than the billions of stars in the clear, night sky..."

"Allah loves you more than the trillions of fish in all the oceans..."

"Allah loves you more than the number of raindrops that fall down from the sky in a storm..."

"Allah loves you more than the billions of people in the entire world..."

"Allah loves you more than the grains of sand on our favorite beach..."

"Allah loves you more than the blades of grass in the meadow we have our picnics in..."

"And do you know how much Mama loves you, my dear, sweet Maymunah?" Her mother asked as she squeezed her tenderly.

Maymunah closed her eyes and hugged her mother tightly, as she said, "More than the stars in the sky, the fish in the ocean, the raindrops that fall down from the sky, all the people in the world, the grains of sand on the beach, and the blades of grass in the meadow?"

Maymunah's mother looked lovingly at her daughter, and nodded her head, "Yes, habeebty. So, so much more than that, and the entire universe and what's in it. But even my love could not measure up to Allah's love for you, for He loves you more than that."

Maymunah beamed with excitement, and more love for Allah than she had ever felt before. *How great is Allah to love me this much?!* Maymunah thought, as she raced back to her room.

She pondered over all the vast creation her mother had mentioned. She thought of how much she loved her Mama, and how much Mama loved her. It was a love bigger than the whole, wide world.

But the biggest love of all was the love Maymunah felt for Allah, subhanahu wa ta'ala. And even bigger than that, was Allah's love for little Maymunah.

For however big or however much Maymunah thought something was, she knew that Allah loved her more than that.

"And He is Oft-forgiving,
All Loving." (Quran 85:14)

Glossary

1. Allah Subhanahu wa ta'la: God the Most Glorified and the Most High is He.

2. Habeebty: a tender phrase, in the Arabic language, meaning, "My love."

3. Quran: Islamic holy book containing the word of Allah revealed to Prophet Muhammad, peace be upon him.

4. Inshallah: Arabic phrase meaning, "If God wills."

About the Author:
Heba Subeh-Hyder is a resident of Southern California and a wife to a loving husband of 15 years, and mother of three wonderful girls.

She has a Bachelor's degree in Management and Human Resources from Cal Poly Pomona, where she was actively involved in the Muslim Student Association, and is currently working on another degree in Islamic Studies from California Islamic University.

Heba has worked as an Executive Team Leader, Office Manager, led a few Islamic halaqas (study circles), and has spoken on panels aimed towards educating the public regarding different topics on Islam.

Her passion for the deen is what inspired her to be an author. Her aim is to nurture our youth's innate belief and love of Allah at a young age, and to encourage reflection by taking them on adventures to discover Allah, subhanahu wa ta'ala through His attributes.

About the Illustrator:
Aatena is currently an upperclassman studying Computer Science. She loves to do art as a hobby! She's done digital art for more than 5 years, and a recently came onto traditional painting, specifically with acrylic paint. Apart from working on her degree and drawing, she loves to game, visit new places, try new kinds of food, and spending time with her cats.

www.ingramcontent.com/pod-product-compliance
Lightning Source LLC
Chambersburg PA
CBHW042147240326
41723CB00014B/617

9 781733 826730